Brilliant practice for Primary pupils with EAL!

This CGP book is packed with practice for Primary pupils who are working towards 'Early Acquisition' (English proficiency Band B).

New language structures are introduced in a clear, friendly way, with scaffolded activities to guide pupils in forming their own sentences.

It doesn't stop there! We've also included free audio files so pupils can listen and repeat — you can find them at this page:

www.cgpbooks.co.uk/EAL-book-two

What CGP is all about

Our sole aim here at CGP is to produce the highest quality books
— carefully written, immaculately presented and
dangerously close to being funny.

Then we work our socks off to get them out to you
— at the cheapest possible prices.

Contents

Part 1

Section 1 — Nouns

Section 2 — Verbs

Section 3 — Adjectives and Adverbs

Section 4 — Reading Comprehension

Section 5 — Maths Language

Part 2 ← Part 2 revisits and builds on what has been learned in Part 1.

About the Authors

Sally Roberts is a KS2 EAL advisor, teacher trainer and Advanced Practitioner in EAL in the East Midlands. She has specialised in second language acquisition for nine years and has supported over 200 KS2 children through the early stages of learning English. She studied Bilingualism and DysTEFL (Dyslexia and TEFL) at the Universities of Birmingham and Lancaster.

Greci Cristina Queiroz Taylor has 15 years' experience in EAL/EFL, having helped over 300 KS2 EAL pupils to "make rapid progress" (Ofsted Report 2017). She has a degree in Linguistics, a CELTA certificate from Cambridge University, a Diploma in Foreign Language Teaching and a Masters degree in Applied Linguistics and ELT from Nottingham University.

Written by Sally Roberts and Greci Cristina Queiroz Taylor.

Editors: Keith Blackhall, Sam Norman, Rosa Roberts, Hayley Shaw.
Reviewed by Juliette Green.
With thanks to Ellen Burton and Glenn Rogers for the proofreading.

Voice artists for online audio tracks: Eben O'Brien, Phoebe Mullen and Sam Norman.

ISBN: 978 1 78908 800 7

Clipart from Corel®
Graphics used throughout the book © www.edu-clips.com
Printed by Elanders Ltd, Newcastle upon Tyne.
Based on the classic CGP style created by Richard Parsons.

How to Use this Book

Working with Children with EAL

- Children will need to work with an adult or '**Helper**' to use this book.

- The same types of activities are **repeated** though, so in time children should be able to complete many tasks **independently**.

- The activities work really well when children work in **pairs** or **small groups**. Encourage the children to read out their work to you, and to each other.

- Involving children **without EAL** in your teaching is also a great idea — these children will learn a lot about the English language from teaching non-native speakers.

Blue and Green Colour-Coding

Most topics are presented over **two pages**.

The **teaching points** on the left-hand pages are split into blue parts and **green parts**.

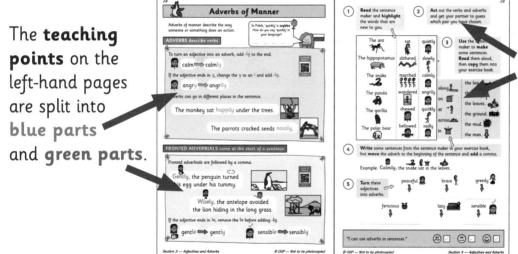

The **activities** on the right-hand pages have the **same colour-coding** to show you which teaching point is being covered.

When a question is in an orange box, it is testing both blue and green content.

- The content in blue is **easier** than the content in green.

- It's a good idea to cover **all the blue content first** — including the activities on the right-hand page — **before** covering the **green content**.

- With some pupils, you might choose to cover **only the blue content** in the first session, leaving the green content until a later date.

How to Use this Book

Features of the pages

Children are introduced to words and structures in other languages and are invited to think about their **first language**.

- This demonstrates to the child that their first language is **valued**.

- It also promotes **metacognitive thinking** and links learning to ideas already familiar to the children.

The language learning begins with some grammar points and vocabulary. You should read through the explanations with the children to help them understand the grammar. There is audio of the vocabulary and phrases on the page for children to **listen to** and **repeat**. You can access the audio tracks by scanning the QR code, or by going to:

www.cgpbooks.co.uk/EAL-book-two

You may prefer to read the content out yourself, without using the recorded audio.

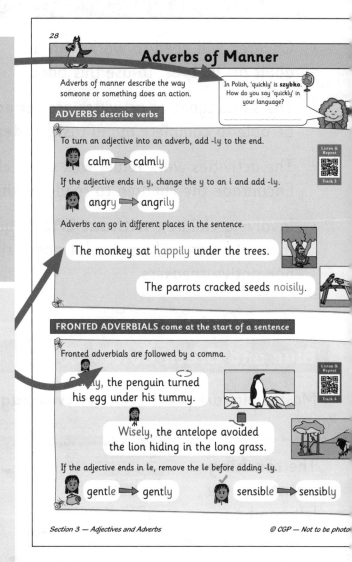

Phonics

Some children may **appear** to read English quite fluently, but inaccuracy in pronunciation can make even known words unintelligible to them — adding to comprehension problems.

- Accurate phonic decoding skills give children the tools they need to extend their own vocabulary through reading.

- **Pages 62-63** have exercises to help children practise the different vowel sounds in English.

- It's a good idea to use these pages regularly to help children practise and develop their phonics skills.

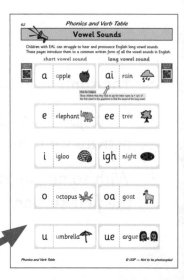

How to Use this Book

How to Use this Book

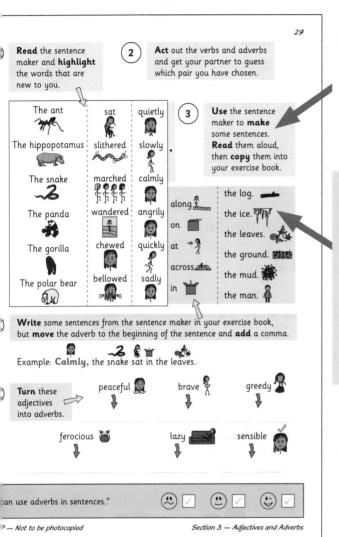

Hints for Helpers give tips on how you can help children further. They will also point out common **errors** made by children with EAL.

Sentence makers like this are a key feature of this book. They enable children to create their own grammatical sentences independently.

To reinforce their learning, encourage children to copy out sentences into an **exercise book**, and then read them back to you, or to each other.

Children with EAL benefit from large amounts of repetition, so it's a good idea not to rush through the activities. Depending on the child's level of English, each topic may take two lessons or more to complete.

Irregular Past Tense Verbs

At the back of the book is a table showing **irregular past tense verb forms**.

Children can use this table as a **reference** when completing written work.

How to Use this Book

Describing People

On these pages, you will practise introducing yourself and others.

The FIRST PERSON is for talking about yourself

When you talk about yourself, you use **I**.

> In Romanian, **numele meu este** means 'my name is'. What do you say in your language?
>
> ....

My **name** is Alex.   I **am** 6 years old.

I **am** from Romania.   I **am** Romanian.

I **speak** Romanian and Roma.

I **have** curly, blond hair and blue eyes.

I **like** football and science.

Listen & Repeat

Track 1

Hint for Helpers
Children might need a reminder that '**I am**', '**he is**' and '**she is**' can be shortened to '**I'm**', '**he's**' and '**she's**'.

The THIRD PERSON is for talking about someone else

When you talk about someone else, you need to change the pronouns and verb forms.

Listen & Repeat

Track 2

I	she	he
am	is	is
have	has	has
speak	speaks	speaks
like	likes	likes

Her **name** is Sara.   She **is** from Pakistan.   She **is** Pakistani.

She **speaks** Urdu and Mirpuri.   She **is** 10.   She **has** straight, brown hair and brown eyes.   She **likes** painting and computer games.

1 **Listen** to Alex and Sara introduce themselves in the first person. **Add** your details in the blue boxes and **read** your story aloud.

Audio Track 3

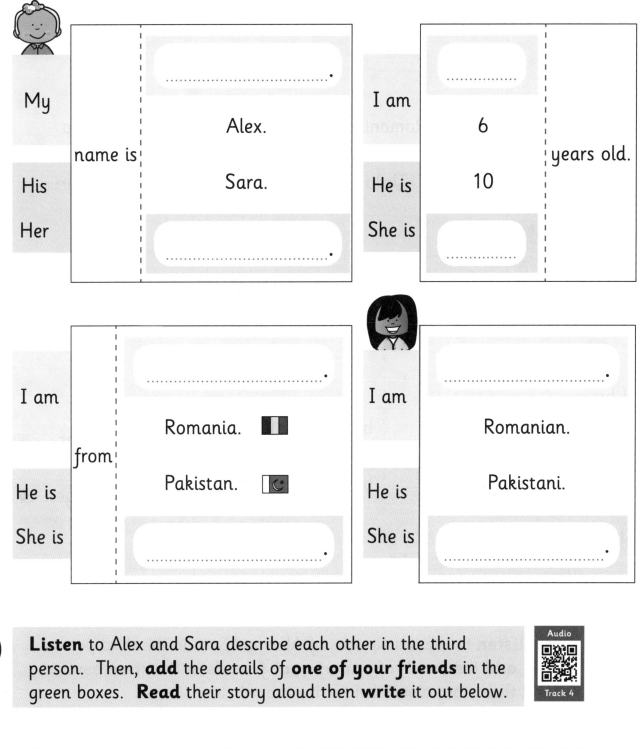

My

His

Her

name is

....

Alex.

Sara.

....

I am

He is

She is

....

6

10

....

years old.

I am

He is

She is

from

....

Romania.

Pakistan.

....

I am

He is

She is

....

Romanian.

Pakistani.

....

2 **Listen** to Alex and Sara describe each other in the third person. Then, **add** the details of **one of your friends** in the green boxes. **Read** their story aloud then **write** it out below.

Audio Track 4

....

....

....

....

....

Describing People

3 **Listen** to Alex and Sara talk about what language they speak and their hair and eyes. **Add** your own details in the blue boxes and **read** the sentences aloud.

Audio
Track 5

I speak	....	and	....
	Romanian		Roma.
He speaks	Urdu		Mirpuri.
She speaks	....		....

I have	....................,	.... hair	and	.... eyes.
	curly, ℓℓℓℓ	blonde hair		blue eyes.
He has	straight, ══	brown hair		brown eyes.
She has	....................,	.... hair		.... eyes.

4 Now **listen** to the descriptions of Alex and Sara in the third person. Then, **add** the details of **one of your friends** in the green boxes. **Read** their story aloud then **write** it out below.

Audio
Track 6

....

....

....

....

....

(5) **Listen** to Alex and Sara talk about school.
Add two things you like and your teacher's name in the blue boxes and **read** your story aloud.

Audio
Track 7

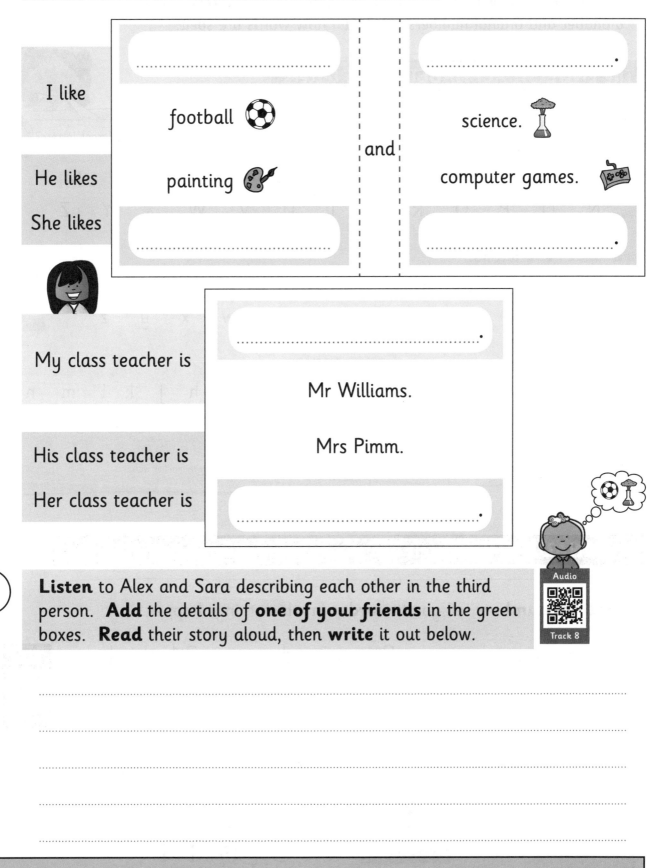

I like

....

....

He likes

football ⚽

and

science. 🧪

painting 🎨

computer games. 🎮

She likes

....

....

My class teacher is

....

Mr Williams.

Mrs Pimm.

His class teacher is

Her class teacher is

....

(6) **Listen** to Alex and Sara describing each other in the third person. **Add** the details of **one of your friends** in the green boxes. **Read** their story aloud, then **write** it out below.

Audio
Track 8

....

....

....

....

....

"I can introduce myself and others."

Describing People

Section 1 — Nouns

The Alphabet & Ordinal Numbers

In this topic, you will practise using the names of the letters of the alphabet and ordinal numbers to explain how words are spelt.

The ENGLISH ALPHABET has 26 letters

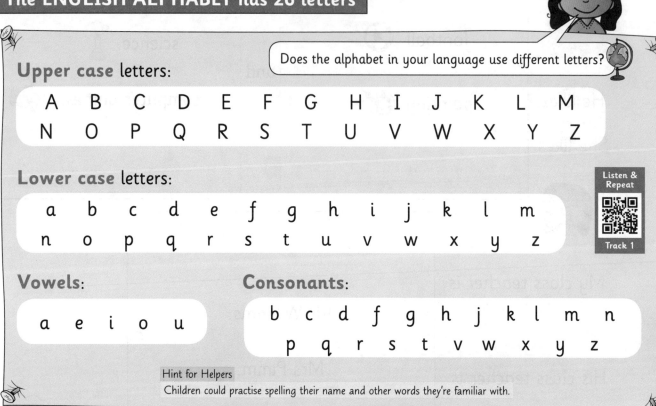

Upper case letters:

A B C D E F G H I J K L M
N O P Q R S T U V W X Y Z

Does the alphabet in your language use different letters?

Lower case letters:

a b c d e f g h i j k l m
n o p q r s t u v w x y z

Listen & Repeat — Track 1

Vowels:

a e i o u

Consonants:

b c d f g h j k l m n
p q r s t v w x y z

Hint for Helpers
Children could practise spelling their name and other words they're familiar with.

ORDINAL NUMBERS tell you the position of something in a list

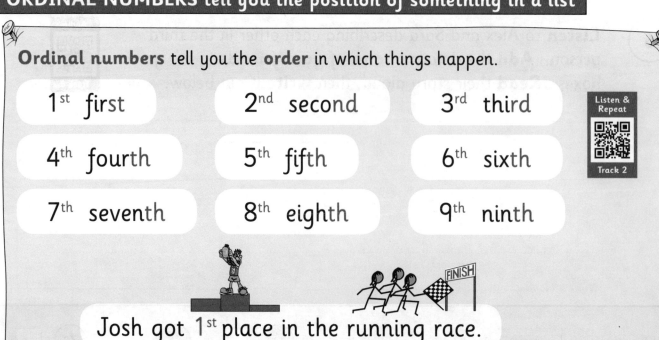

Ordinal numbers tell you the **order** in which things happen.

1st first	2nd second	3rd third
4th fourth	5th fifth	6th sixth
7th seventh	8th eighth	9th ninth

Listen & Repeat — Track 2

Josh got 1st place in the running race.

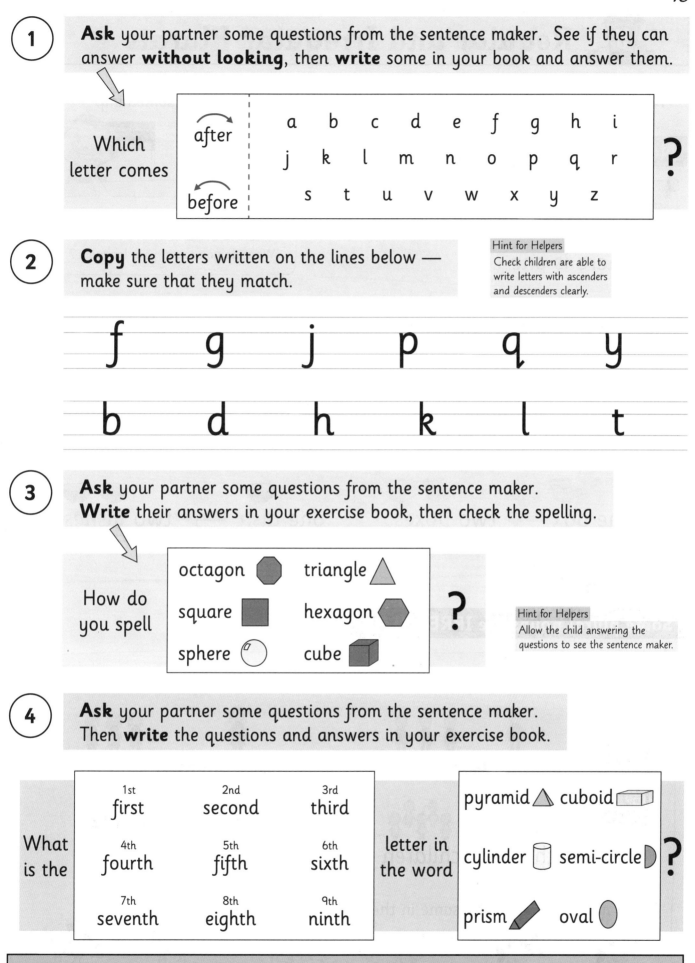

(1) **Ask** your partner some questions from the sentence maker. See if they can answer **without looking**, then **write** some in your book and answer them.

Which letter comes

after | a b c d e f g h i
j k l m n o p q r
before | s t u v w x y z

?

(2) **Copy** the letters written on the lines below — make sure that they match.

Hint for Helpers
Check children are able to write letters with ascenders and descenders clearly.

f   g   j   p   q   y

b   d   h   k   l   t

(3) **Ask** your partner some questions from the sentence maker.
Write their answers in your exercise book, then check the spelling.

How do you spell

octagon ⬡   triangle △
square ■   hexagon ⬡
sphere ◯   cube ◻

?

Hint for Helpers
Allow the child answering the questions to see the sentence maker.

(4) **Ask** your partner some questions from the sentence maker.
Then **write** the questions and answers in your exercise book.

What is the

1st first	2nd second	3rd third
4th fourth	5th fifth	6th sixth
7th seventh	8th eighth	9th ninth

letter in the word

pyramid △ cuboid ◻
cylinder ⬭ semi-circle ◗
prism ▱ oval ◯

?

"I can spell words with the letters of the alphabet and use ordinal numbers."

Regular and Irregular Plurals

Nouns usually change spelling when they refer to more than one of something.

Nouns have a SINGULAR and PLURAL form

Singular nouns refer to one thing.

There is one cup.

> In German, '1 book' is **ein Buch** and '2 books' is **zwei Bücher**. What do you say in your language?

Listen & Repeat — Track 3

You add an **s** to most nouns to make them plural.

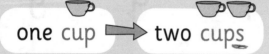

one cup ➡ two cup**s**

If the noun ends in **ch**, **sh**, **o**, **x** or **s**, you add **es**.

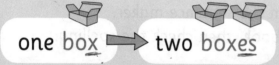

one box ➡ two box**es**

one dish ➡ two dish**es**

Some plural nouns are IRREGULAR

Some plural nouns don't end in **s**.

Listen & Repeat — Track 4

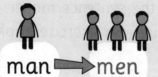

man ➡ men

woman ➡ women

child ➡ children

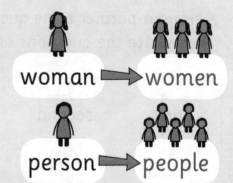

person ➡ people

Some nouns are spelt the same in the singular and plural.

fish ➡ fish

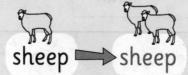

sheep ➡ sheep

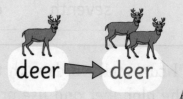

deer ➡ deer

1 **Read** the sentence maker and **highlight** the words that are new to you.

2 **Write** some sentences in your exercise book. Make sure you use the **singular** and **plural** forms of nouns.

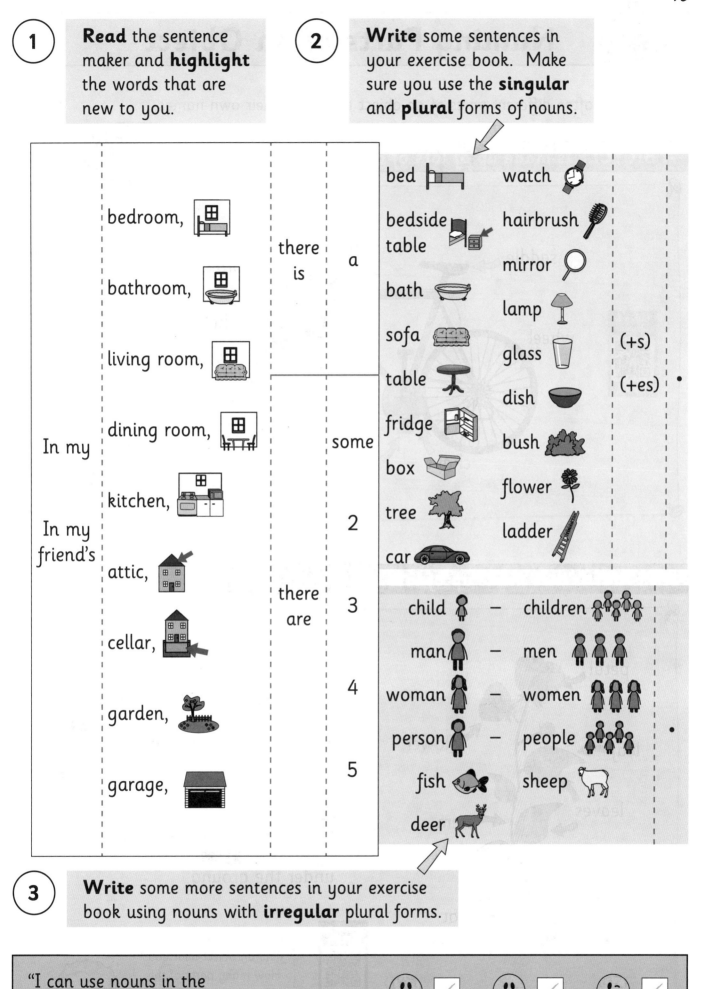

3 **Write** some more sentences in your exercise book using nouns with **irregular** plural forms.

"I can use nouns in the singular and plural form."

Naming Parts of an Object

There are often different parts of an object that have their own names.

A BICYCLE is made up of lots of different parts

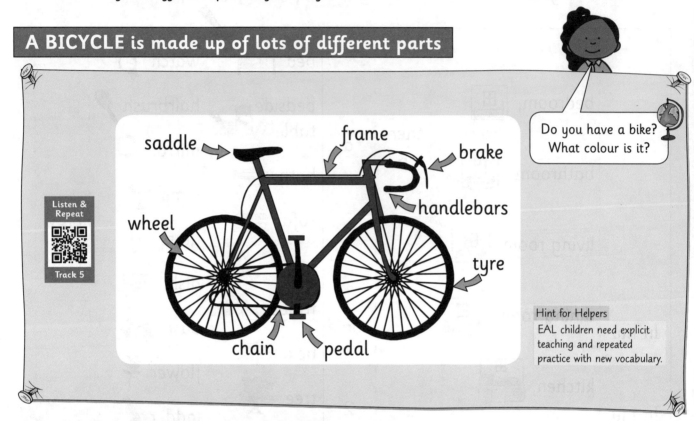

Listen & Repeat
Track 5

Do you have a bike? What colour is it?

Hint for Helpers
EAL children need explicit teaching and repeated practice with new vocabulary.

A PLANT is also made up of lots of different parts

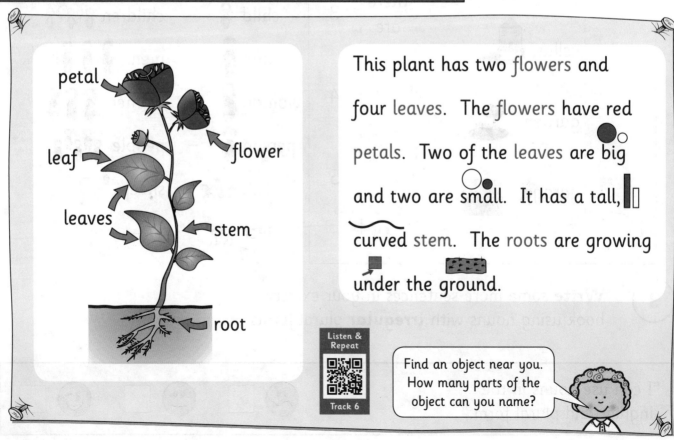

This plant has two flowers and four leaves. The flowers have red petals. Two of the leaves are big and two are small. It has a tall, curved stem. The roots are growing under the ground.

Listen & Repeat
Track 6

Find an object near you. How many parts of the object can you name?

1 **Play** a game with your partner. You will need a pencil each and a dice.

Roll the dice and say the name of the bicycle part that matches the number, then draw it in your box. Now your partner rolls the dice. The first person to draw a complete bike wins!

 frame   wheel   pedal

 chain   handlebars   saddle

Hint for Helpers
This game can be adapted to teach all sorts of vocabulary.

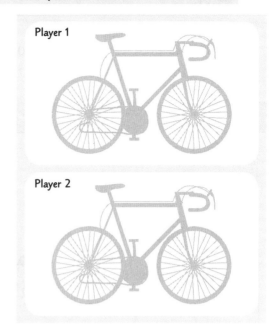
Player 1

Player 2

2 **Choose** one of the bikes below. Get your partner to **ask** questions to work out which one you're thinking of.

Does it have a | red ☀ blue ☀ green ☀ yellow ☀ | saddle ⚊ frame ◺ ?

Does it have | pedals ⚊ wheels ◉ handlebars ⤵ ?

3 **Draw** your own plant. **Write** some sentences about it below.

My Plant has five red flowers and
It has nine green leaves and
It has a tall brown stem and
It has a bown roots and

veny gud

"I can describe parts of an object."   ✓   ✓   ✓

Section 1 — Nouns

Regular Simple Past Tense

The simple past tense is used to talk about things that are finished and in the past.

> In Italian, 'yesterday' is **ieri**.
> How do you say 'yesterday' in your language?
> ....

Add -ed to REGULAR verbs

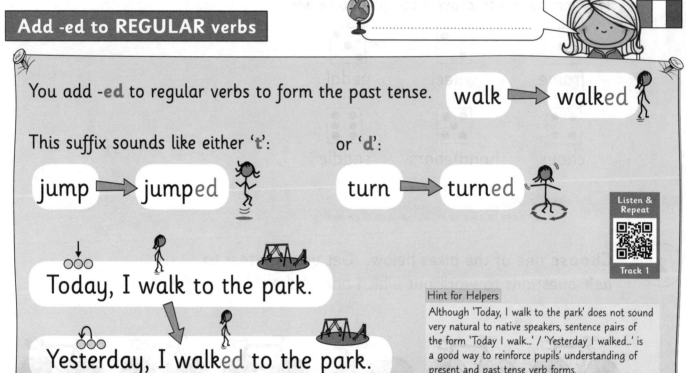

You add -**ed** to regular verbs to form the past tense. walk ➡ walk**ed**

This suffix sounds like either '**t**':   or '**d**':

jump ➡ jump**ed**   turn ➡ turn**ed**

Today, I walk to the park.

Yesterday, I walk**ed** to the park.

Listen & Repeat
Track 1

Hint for Helpers
Although 'Today, I walk to the park' does not sound very natural to native speakers, sentence pairs of the form 'Today I walk...' / 'Yesterday I walked...' is a good way to reinforce pupils' understanding of present and past tense verb forms.

The -ed part of the VERB sometimes sounds like 'id'

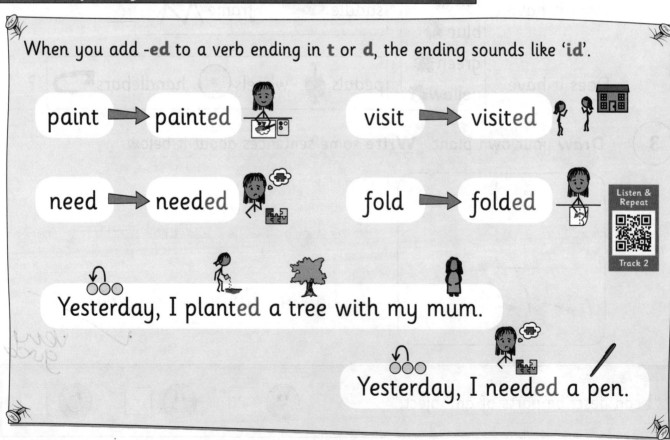

When you add -**ed** to a verb ending in **t** or **d**, the ending sounds like '**id**'.

paint ➡ paint**ed**   visit ➡ visit**ed**

need ➡ need**ed**   fold ➡ fold**ed**

Listen & Repeat
Track 2

Yesterday, I plant**ed** a tree with my mum.

Yesterday, I need**ed** a pen.

1 **Read** the sentence maker and **highlight** the words that are new to you.

2 **Write** some pairs of present and past tense sentences in your exercise book. **Read** each pair of sentences **aloud** after you've written them.

Example: Today, I walk to the shop.
Yesterday, I walked to the shop.

Hint for Helpers
Children could add
ideas of their own.

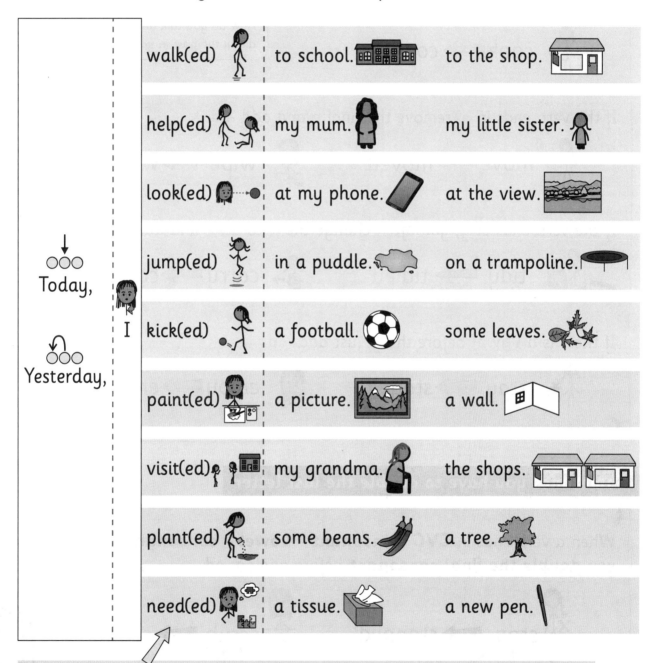

3 **Write** some sentence pairs using the green part of the sentence maker in your exercise book, then **read** them aloud carefully to your partner.

"I can make sentences which use the simple past tense."

Section 2 — Verbs

More Regular Simple Past Tense

There are some spelling rules you need to follow when writing in the simple past tense.

Sometimes you have to add or remove letters

Sometimes you have to add or remove letters

Some verbs just add **-ed**.

 cook ➡ cook**ed**

> How do you talk about what you did in the past in your language?

If the verb ends in **e**, remove the final **e** and add **-ed**.

move ➡ mov**ed**

 wipe ➡ wip**ed**

Listen & Repeat Track 3

If the verb ends in **y**, you often change the **y** to an **i**, and add **-ed**.

 tidy ➡ tid**ied**

 carry ➡ carr**ied**

If there is a **vowel** before the **y**, just add **-ed**.

 stay ➡ stay**ed**

 enjoy ➡ enjoy**ed**

Sometimes you have to double the last letter

When a verb ends in **CVC** (**consonant – vowel – consonant**), you **double the final consonant** before adding **-ed**.

Vowels
a e i o u

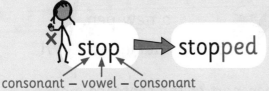 stop ➡ stop**ped**
consonant – vowel – consonant

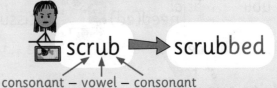 scrub ➡ scrub**bed**
consonant – vowel – consonant

Listen & Repeat Track 4

 Sa Su

At the weekend, my brother scrub**bed** the table.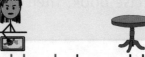

Hint for Helpers
You don't double the last consonant if it's **w**, **x** or **y**.

1 **Read** the sentence maker and **highlight** the words that are new to you.

2 **Write** sentences in the simple past tense in your exercise book, then **read** them to your partner.

Hint for Helpers
As they grow in confidence, children can use ideas of their own.

| At the weekend, | I / my mum / my dad / my brother / my sister | cook / clean / wash / change / wipe / carr~~y~~i / empt~~y~~i / tid~~y~~i / enjoy / scrub +b / mop +p | +ed | some chicken. / the bath. / the dishes. / the sheets. / the table. / my toys upstairs. / the bins. / my bedroom. / the match. / the sink. / up a spill. | the dinner. / the toilet. / the floor. / the towels. / the hob. / the shopping from the car. / the laundry basket. / the desk. / the weather. / the table. / the tiles. |

3 **Write** some more sentences using the verbs that double the final letter in the simple past tense.

4 **Circle** the verbs which double the final letter before adding **-ed**. **Write** a simple past tense sentence in your exercise book for each verb you circle.

jump   hop   grab   rub   bang   chop

"I can use regular verbs in the simple past." ☹ ✓   🙂 ✓   😉 ✓

Irregular Verbs in the Simple Past

Some verbs don't end in **-ed** in the past tense. They're said to be 'irregular' because they don't follow the normal pattern.

IRREGULAR past tense verbs

Irregular verbs do not end in **-ed** in the past tense.

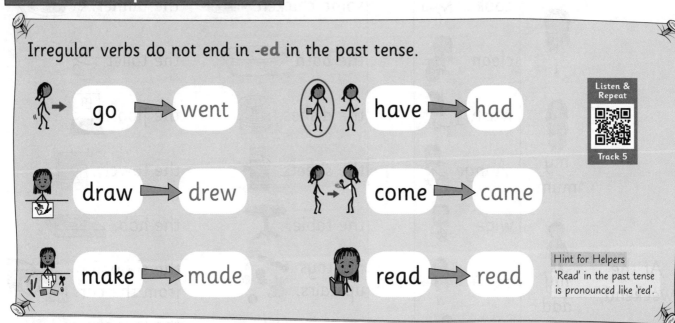

go → went

have → had

draw → drew

come → came

make → made

read → read

Listen & Repeat
Track 5

Hint for Helpers
'Read' in the past tense is pronounced like 'red'.

In French, the days of the week are **lundi, mardi, mercredi, jeudi, vendredi, samedi, dimanche**. What do you say in your language?

ADVERBIALS of time

Adverbials of time use different prepositions (e.g. in, on, at).

Months of the year use **in**.

 In July, I went to the beach.

Days of the week use **on**.

On Thursday, I made a cake.

At the weekend is a set phrase.

At the weekend, I read a new book.

Months of the Year

January	July
February	August
March	September
April	October
May	November
June	December

Hint for Helpers
You can find songs online to help children remember the months.

Listen & Repeat
Track 6

(1) **Read** the sentence maker and **highlight** the words that are new to you.

(2) **Write** some pairs of present and past tense sentences in your exercise book. **Read** each pair of sentences **aloud** after you've written them.

Example: Today, I go to the city. Yesterday, I went to the city.

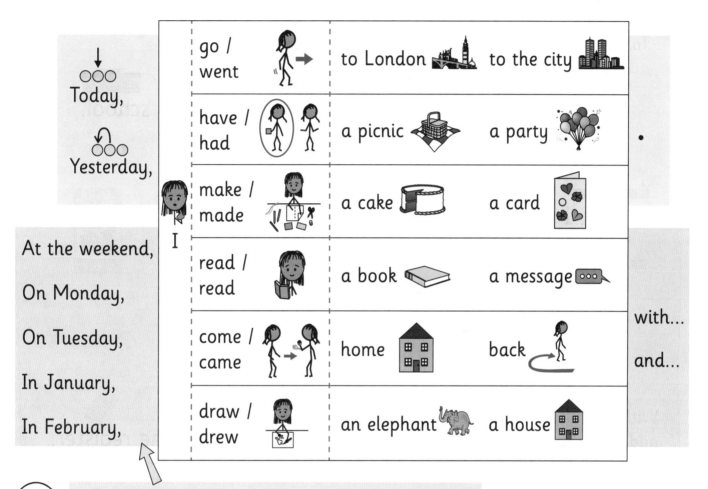

↓
○○○
Today,

↺
○○○
Yesterday,

At the weekend,

On Monday,

On Tuesday,

In January,

In February,

I

with...

and...

(3) **Write** some simple past tense sentences using different adverbials of time in your exercise book.

Examples:

On Wednesday, I drew an elephant and coloured it in.

In March, I made a card with my sister.

"I can use irregular verbs in the simple past." 🙁 ✓　🙂 ✓　😉 ✓

　　　　　　　　　Section 2 — Verbs

Putting Events in Order with the Simple Present

On these pages, you will learn to talk about what you and your friends do every day.

In Brazil, school starts very early and ends at lunchtime. Do you know what school is like in a different country?

ADVERBIALS OF TIME and the SIMPLE PRESENT

To say the order you do things in, start your sentence with an **adverbial of time**:

At 8:30 in the morning, I go to school.

then use the **simple present tense**:

First, I line up with my classmates.

Next, I answer the register.

Before I go outside to play, I do my work.

With the third person singular (**he/she/it**), add **-s** to the end of the verb.

She answers the register.

Listen & Repeat — Track 7

Be careful with the SPELLING of verbs in the THIRD PERSON

If verbs end in **o**, **ch** or **sh**, you add **-es** when it's in the **third person singular**.

I go to school. ➡ My friend goes to school.

I watch TV. ➡ My sister watches TV.

Listen & Repeat — Track 8

If verbs end with a **consonant** and **y**, you change the **y** to an **i** and add **-es**.

We carry our books home. ➡ She carries her books home.

1 **Number** the parts of the sentences in the right order, then **write** the sentences in your exercise book.

a) ◯ morning, ◯ up. ①In ◯ I ◯ the ◯ line

b) ◯ peg. ◯ I ◯ put my ◯ a ◯ Next, ◯ coat on

c) ◯ Mr Smith ◯ our ◯ Before ◯ teaches ◯ lessons ◯ playtime,

d) ◯ outside ◯ we ◯ to ◯ go ◯ play. ◯ Then,

e) ◯ maths lesson, ◯ After ◯ our ◯ we ◯ lunch. ◯ have

f) ◯ school, ◯ After ◯ me ◯ walks ◯ my uncle ◯ home.

2 Use the sentence maker to **write** about your friend's school day.

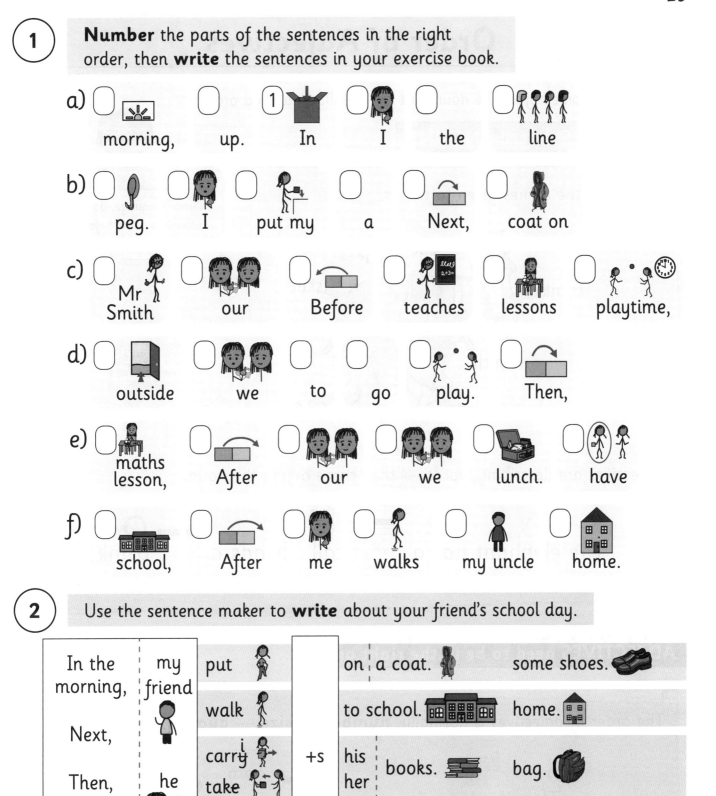

"I can use the present tense."

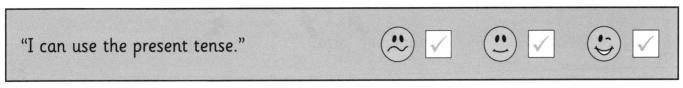

© CGP — Not to be photocopied

Section 2 — Verbs

Order of Adjectives

Adjectives come before the noun and are usually in a fixed order.

ADJECTIVES describe NOUNS

Nouns are the names given to things.

In your language, do the adjectives come before or after the noun?

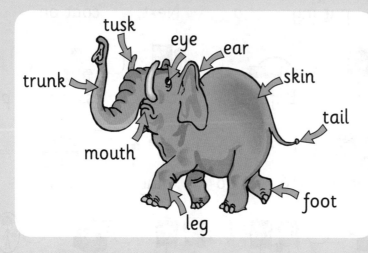

tusk
eye
ear
trunk
skin
tail
mouth
foot
leg

Listen & Repeat — Track 1

Adjectives are describing words — they come before the noun.

The elephant has a short tail. It has a long trunk.

ADJECTIVES need to be in the right order

The order of adjectives is normally: **number** — **size** — **quality**.

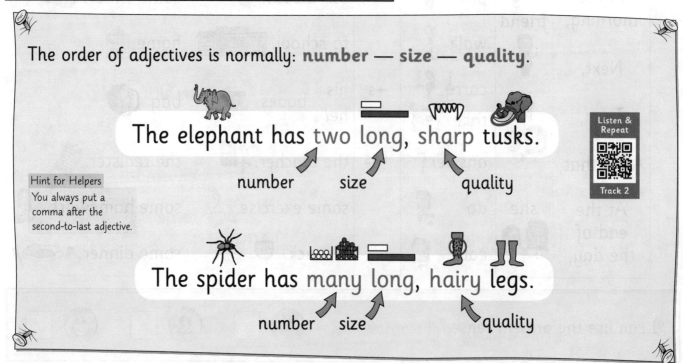

The elephant has two long, sharp tusks.

number   size   quality

Listen & Repeat — Track 2

Hint for Helpers
You always put a comma after the second-to-last adjective.

The spider has many long, hairy legs.

number   size   quality

1 **Play** a game of **charades** by choosing an animal and an adjective to act out while your partner guesses.

2 **Read** the sentence maker and **highlight** the words that are new to you.

elephant	eagle
ostrich	spider
fish	tiger
rhinoceros	giraffe
beetle	penguin
tortoise	horse

The ... has (a)

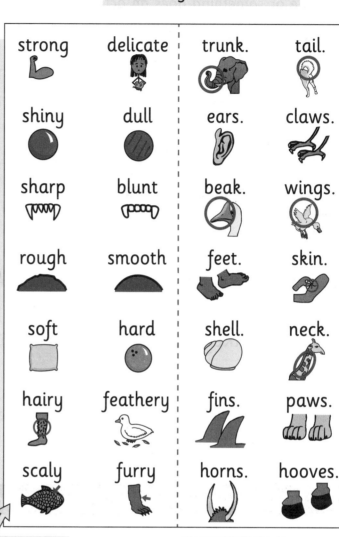

strong, delicate, shiny, dull, sharp, blunt, rough, smooth, soft, hard, hairy, feathery, scaly, furry

trunk. tail. ears. claws. beak. wings. feet. skin. shell. neck. fins. paws. horns. hooves.

3 **Use** the sentence maker to **make** some sentences. **Write** them in your exercise book and **read** them aloud.

4 **Write** some animal sentences in your exercise book using three adjectives in the correct order. **Use** these adjectives of size to help you.

long, short, small, tiny, enormous, large, tall

Example:

number → ← size

A rhinoceros has two short, powerful horns.

↖ quality

"I can put adjectives in the right order."

Section 3 — Adjectives and Adverbs

Adverbs of Manner

Adverbs of manner describe the way someone or something does an action.

In Polish, 'quickly' is **szybko**. How do you say 'quickly' in your language?

....

ADVERBS describe verbs

To turn an adjective into an adverb, add **-ly** to the end.

 calm ➡ calmly

Listen & Repeat
Track 3

If the adjective ends in **y**, change the **y** to an **i** and add **-ly**.

 angry ➡ angrily

Adverbs can go in different places in the sentence.

The monkey sat happily under the trees.

The parrots cracked seeds noisily.

FRONTED ADVERBIALS come at the start of a sentence

Fronted adverbials are followed by a comma.

Gently, the penguin turned his egg under his tummy.

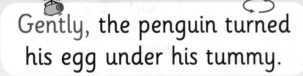

Listen & Repeat
Track 4

Wisely, the antelope avoided the lion hiding in the long grass.

If the adjective ends in **le**, remove the **le** before adding **-ly**.

 gentle ➡ gently

 sensible ➡ sensibly

Section 3 — Adjectives and Adverbs　　　　　　　　© CGP — Not to be photocopied

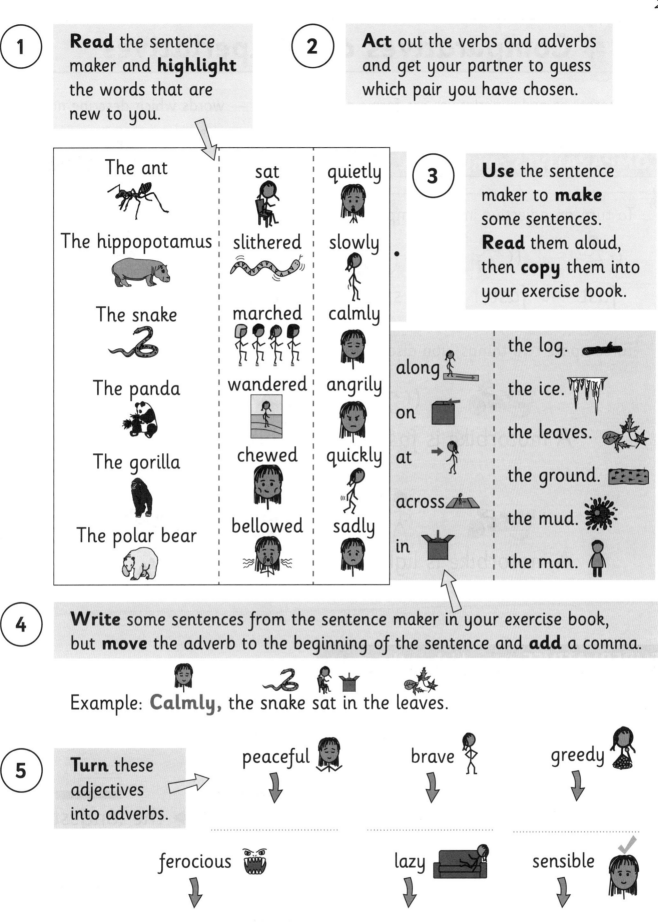

① **Read** the sentence maker and **highlight** the words that are new to you.

② **Act** out the verbs and adverbs and get your partner to guess which pair you have chosen.

③ **Use** the sentence maker to **make** some sentences. **Read** them aloud, then **copy** them into your exercise book.

The ant — sat — quietly
The hippopotamus — slithered — slowly
The snake — marched — calmly
The panda — wandered — angrily
The gorilla — chewed — quickly
The polar bear — bellowed — sadly

along — on — at — across — in

the log. — the ice. — the leaves. — the ground. — the mud. — the man.

④ **Write** some sentences from the sentence maker in your exercise book, but **move** the adverb to the beginning of the sentence and **add** a comma.

Example: **Calmly,** the snake sat in the leaves.

⑤ **Turn** these adjectives into adverbs.

peaceful ....

brave ....

greedy ....

ferocious ....

lazy ....

sensible ....

"I can use adverbs in sentences."

Comparatives and Superlatives

Comparatives and superlatives are forms of **adjectives** — words which describe nouns.

COMPARATIVES compare one thing with another

To turn an adjective into a comparative, add **er**:

fast ➡ faster

small ➡ smaller

> In Spanish, 'faster than' is **más rápido que**. Can you say this in your language?

To compare two things, you also need the word **than**:

A motorbike is faster than a bike.

Listen & Repeat — Track 5

A motorbike is lighter than a lorry.

Watch Out!
⬤○ big ➡ bigger
heavy ➡ heavyer

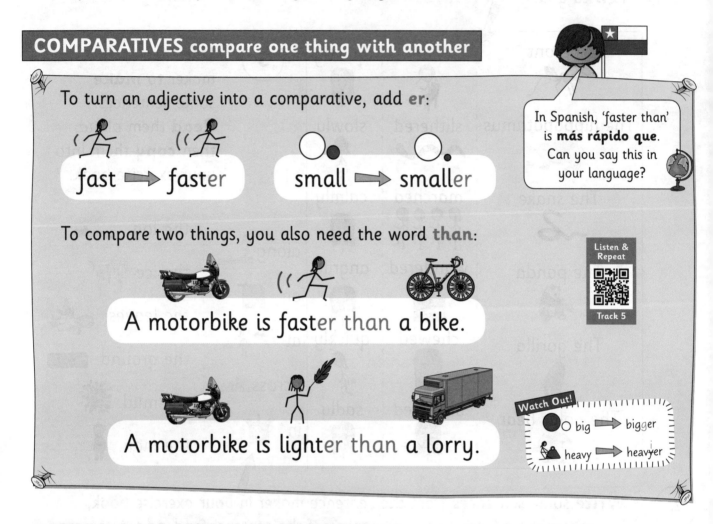

SUPERLATIVES say which is the most

The superlative is formed by: **the** + adjective + **est**.

small ➡ the smallest

long ➡ the longest

The aeroplane is the longest.

Listen & Repeat — Track 6

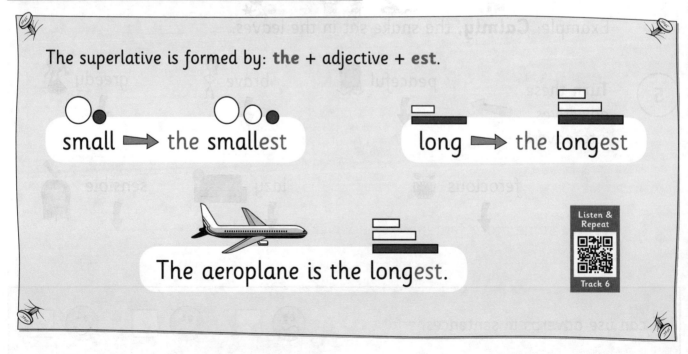

Hint for Helpers
Children could then copy some
sentences in their exercise book.

1   **Read** and **discuss**. **Say** some sentences.

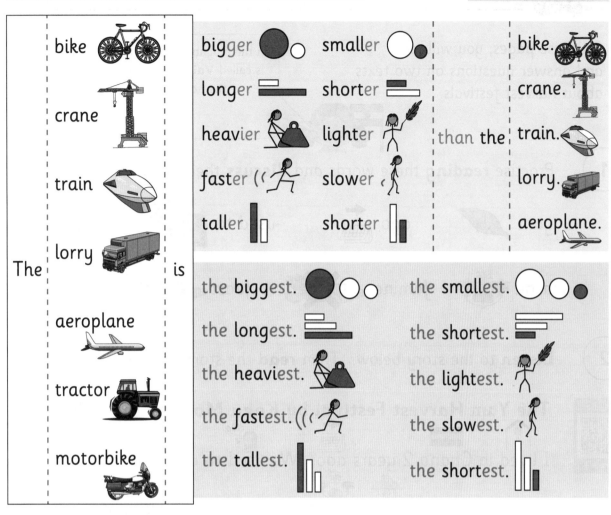

The | bike / crane / train / lorry / aeroplane / tractor / motorbike | is | bigger / smaller / longer / shorter / heavier / lighter / faster / slower / taller / shorter | than the | bike. / crane. / train. / lorry. / aeroplane.

the biggest. / the smallest. / the longest. / the shortest. / the heaviest. / the lightest. / the fastest. / the slowest. / the tallest. / the shortest.

2   **Draw** and **write** your favourite sentences.

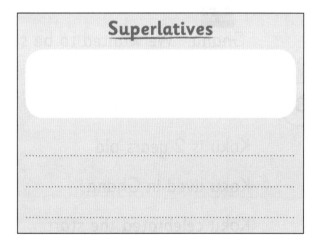

Comparatives

Superlatives

3   **Write** some more sentences in your exercise book.
Read them aloud to your partner.

"I can use comparatives and superlatives."

   Section 3 — Adjectives and Adverbs

Section 4 — Reading Comprehension

Harvest Festival

On these pages, you will read and answer questions on two texts about harvest festivals.

In the Punjab region of India, the harvest festival is called **Vaisakhi**. Does your family celebrate the harvest? What do you call it?

....

(1) Practise **reading** these words and **discuss** their meanings.

yam   ago   used to   celebrate

season   famine   feast   parade

(2) **Listen** to the story below. Then **read** the story to yourself.

Audio
Track 1

The Yam Harvest Festival by Koku Moyoyo (aged 8)

I lived in Ghana 2 years ago. We used to celebrate the yam harvest at the end of the rainy season. We had huge feasts, dances, story-telling and parades. Yams are a very important food in Ghana. We wanted to be sure there wouldn't be a famine next year.

(3) **Answer** with 'true' or 'false'.

Koku is 2 years old. ...*false* ✓   People told stories. ...*true*...

Koku lived in Ghana. ...*true*... ✓   People had races. ...*false*...

Koku celebrated the start of the rainy season. ...*false*...   People had dances. ...*true*...

Koku celebrated the yam harvest. ...*true*...   Yams are important in Ghana. ...*true*...

Koku celebrated the end of the rainy season. ...*true*...   People wanted a famine. ...*false*...

17/12/20

4 Practise **reading** these words and **discuss** their meanings.

Indonesia(n)   celebrated   harvest   rice

offerings   statue   fields   races

5 **Listen** to Siti's story. Then **read** the story to yourself.

The Rice Harvest Festival by Siti Saputra (aged 10)

When I was 8 years old, I lived in Bali, in Indonesia. We celebrated the Rice Harvest Festival. We made offerings to Dewi Sri, the Hindu rice goddess. We put statues of her in the fields, decorated our town with coloured flags and held bull races. We had a lot of fun. It was a happy time.

Audio
Track 2

6 **Answer** with '**true**' or '**false**'.
Rewrite the statements correctly using the text.

true ✓
false x

1. Indonesia is in Bali. *false* ✓

2. Siti lives in Bali now. *True* ✓

3. Dewi Sri made offerings to Siti. *~~true~~ false* ✓

4. Siti put statues in the fields. *True* ✓

5. They held bull fights. *false* ✓

"I can answer questions about different harvest festivals."

Numbers 13-30

These pages teach the numbers 13-30 and the vocabulary needed to do addition and subtraction.

In English, the numbers between 13 and 19 all end in **teen**. What is the pattern in your language?

13 to 20

Hint for Helpers
Make sure children know numbers 0-12 well before beginning this topic.

Here are the numbers from 13 to 20 written using digits and words.

13 thirteen
14 fourteen
15 fifteen
16 sixteen
17 seventeen
18 eighteen
19 nineteen
20 twenty

These are the words for **+**, **−** and **=**.

+   plus   add

−   minus   take away

=   equals

Hint for Helpers
Check children can hear and understand the difference between the '**teen**' sound in the numbers 13-19 and the '**ty**' sound in numbers like 20.

Listen & Repeat
Track 1

21 to 30

Here are the numbers from 21 to 30 written using digits and words.

21 twenty-one
22 twenty-two
23 twenty-three
24 twenty-four
25 twenty-five

26 twenty-six
27 twenty-seven
28 twenty-eight
29 twenty-nine
30 thirty

Listen & Repeat
Track 2

These words are also used to mean **+** and **−**.

+   increase ... by ...

$19 + 6 = 25$

Increase 19 by 6. ➡ 25

−   subtract ... from ...

$24 − 3 = 21$

Subtract 3 from 24. ➡ 21

1 **Write** four number sentences in your exercise book.
Read them to your partner.

0		0
1	plus	1
2	**+**	2
3	add	3
4		4
5		5
6		6
7		7
8	minus	8
9	**—** take away	9
10		10

= equals

0	
1	11
2	12
3	13
4	14
5	15
6	16
7	17
8	18
9	19
10	20

2 **Read** the number sentences below to your partner using the word that matches the colour from the table above.

a) $0 + 20 = 20$ b) $17 - 2 = 15$ c) $12 + 8 = 20$ d) $18 - 2 = 16$

e) $3 + 16 = 19$ f) $14 - 3 = 11$ g) $18 - 5 = 13$ h) $13 + 0 = 13$

3 In your exercise book, **write** the number sentences above in words.

4 **Write** these number sentences in your exercise book in the right order so they make the answer shown on the right.

a) by   twenty   Increase   seven.   → 27

b) twenty-eight.   from   six   Subtract   → 22

c) seventeen   by   Increase   nine.   → 26

5 **Read** the sentences above to your partner, then **write** some of your own number sentences for them to answer.

"I know the numbers 13-30 and how to add and subtract numbers."

Section 5 — Maths Language

Using Do and Don't

These pages show you how to talk about school subjects that you and others like and don't like.

In Urdu, 'I like Maths' is
مجھے ریاضی پسند ہے
(mujhay rayazi pasand hai).
How do you say this in your language?

Making a sentence negative

To make a negative sentence, you add **don't** or **doesn't** between the subject and the verb.

I like Maths. → I **don't** like Maths.

subject   verb

Listen & Repeat

Track 1

Raj likes Maths. → Raj **doesn't** like Maths.

subject   verb

Hint for Helpers
Make sure children say and write the verb after 'don't' or 'doesn't' in the **infinitive**, and not, for example: 'Raj doesn't likes maths.'

Asking questions and joining sentences together

You can start a question with **do** or **does**.

Use **do** with **I**, **you**, **they** and **we**.

Use **does** with **he**, **she**, **it** and **names**.

Do you like Maths?

Does Raj like Maths?

School Subjects

Maths
English
Science
Art
History
Geography
PE

You can use conjunctions like **and**, **or** and **but** to talk about more than one thing in a sentence.

Raj likes Maths and he likes English.

Raj likes Maths but he doesn't like English.

☺ and ☺
☺ but ☹
☹ or ☹

Listen & Repeat

Track 2

Raj doesn't like Maths or English.

Hint for Helpers
You only need to write an object after 'or'.

1 The **Venn diagram** below shows who likes Science and who likes Art. Use the sentence maker to **write** about the children in the Venn diagram.

Andre

Likes Science

Likes Art

Raj

Mehin

Ali

Ramisha

Ali		Art.
Andre	likes ☺	
Raj		
Mehin	doesn't like ☹	
Ramisha		Science.
I	like ☺	
	don't like ☹	

Hint for Helpers
You might need to explain to children how a Venn diagram works.

2 **Add** your own name to the Venn diagram, then **write** two sentences about yourself.

....

....

3 **Draw** a Venn diagram in your exercise book. **Label** one circle with a school subject you **like** and the other circle with a subject you **don't like**.

4 **Ask** 4 people if they like each of the school subjects you've chosen. Ask them: "Do you like ... ?" **Write** their names and your name in the Venn diagram.

5 **Write** some sentences about your Venn diagram in your exercise book.

Examples:

☺ 🧪

I like Science but Ben doesn't like Science.

☺ 🎨

Uzma likes Art but she doesn't like History.

☹ 📖 ☹ 🌍

Chloe doesn't like English or Geography.

"I can talk about which subjects my friends like and don't like."

Question Words & Exclamation Marks

Questions often begin with special question words.
Exclamation marks have several different uses.

QUESTION WORDS come at the start of a question

There are different question words
for asking for different information.

Who   **What / Which**   **When**

In Czech, 'Where are you?' is **Kde jsi?**.
How do you say this in your language?

....

Hint for Helpers
'How many' is used for countable
nouns and 'how much' for
uncountable nouns.

Where   **Why**   **How**   **How many**   **How much**

question word → What do you like to eat? ← You always end a question with a question mark.

EXCLAMATION MARKS show loud voices and strong feelings

Sometimes the words **what** and **how** are used in **exclamations**.

What a good idea!   How fantastic!

You can use an **exclamation mark** to show loud voices or shouting.

Hey! I'm over here!   Stop that right now!

You can also use an **exclamation mark** to show strong feelings.

I'm so excited!   I'm really angry about this!

1 Make some sentences using the sentence maker.
Then write them in your exercise book.

Who	is your favourite	singer sportsperson	?
What	do you do	after school when it's sunny	?
Where	do you like to	read sing go on holiday	?
When	do you like to	read go to the supermarket	?
How many		brothers sisters do you have ?

2 Ask 3 people to answer the questions you've made.
Write their answers in your exercise book.

3 Read this text and add full stops, question marks and exclamation marks in the right places. Then answer the questions.

What a disaster [?] The jewellery shop on Main Street owned by Mr Gold has been burgled [.] It happened on Saturday night at 8 pm [.] The burglars got in through a broken window [.] 3 precious rings were stolen []

Mr Gold said, "I'm horrified [] Who will stop these thieves [] "

Who owns the jewellery shop? Mr gold ✓

What happened at the shop? It has been burgled ✓

Where is the shop? Main Street ✓

When did the burglary happen? night at 8 pm ✓

How did the burglars get in? 3 precious ring   a broken window

"I can use question words and exclamation marks correctly."

Question Word Order

The verb 'to be' is often used when asking and answering questions.

The verb 'to be' always comes first in a question

In a statement the verb comes after the subject, but it comes **before** the subject in a question.

> How would you ask these questions in your language? What order would the subject and verb be in?

subject

statement: Julian is at the greengrocer's.

question: Is Julian at the greengrocer's?

You follow the same rules when the sentence is in the past tense.

Hint for Helpers
Make sure children are confident with the different forms of 'to be' in the present and simple past tenses.

statement: Mum and Dad were at the pharmacy.

question: Were Mum and Dad at the pharmacy?

Listen & Repeat
Track 5

Verbs that follow 'to' are always in the infinitive

Verbs that follow **to** are in the **infinitive**, even when the sentence is in the past tense.

Hint for Helpers
The infinitive is the form of the verb that you would find in a dictionary. For example, 'go' and 'be' are **infinitives**, but 'goes' and 'were' are **finite** verb forms.

Mario and Antonio were at the florist's

because they needed to buy some flowers.

Listen & Repeat
Track 6

Mum was at the post office because

she needed to send a letter.

Hint for Helpers
It's a common mistake for children to write e.g. 'she needed to bought' instead of 'she needed to buy'.

1 **Write** a question for the people in the sentence maker.

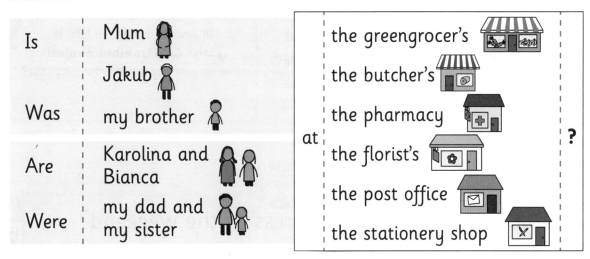

2 **Look** at the table below. Use the information to **answer** your questions.

3 **Rearrange** these sentences in the right order.
Write them in your exercise book.

a)

butcher's because   some meat.   Mum was   at the   she needed   to get

b)

needs to send   My brother is   post office   a letter.   at the   because he

4 In your exercise book, **write** a sentence about Karolina and Bianca
and a sentence about Jakub which include the word 'because'.

"I can use the verb 'to be' to
ask and answer questions."

Section 7 — More Verbs

Did and Didn't

'Did' and 'didn't' are used when asking and answering questions in the simple past tense.

In Arabic, 'I rode my bike' is
ركبت دراجتي (**rakibtu dirajati**).
How do you say this in your language?

....

'Did' and 'didn't' use the infinitive

Did is used to ask questions in the past tense.

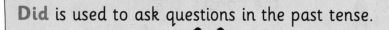

Did your mum buy a new dress at the weekend?

Listen & Repeat — Track 1

Didn't is used in negative sentences.

My mum didn't buy a new dress at the weekend.

The words **did** and **didn't** are followed by an **infinitive**.

sit

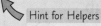

My mum didn't ~~sat~~ on the sofa.

> Hint for Helpers
> Make sure children don't write both verbs in the simple past tense.

How to answer questions in the simple past tense

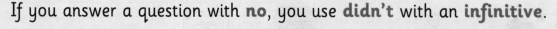

Did your cousin take a photo at the weekend?

Listen & Repeat — Track 2

If you answer a question with **no**, you use **didn't** with an **infinitive**.

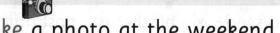

No, my cousin didn't take a photo at the weekend.

If you answer a question with **yes**, you just use the **simple past tense**.

Yes, my cousin took a photo at the weekend.

① **Read** the sentence maker and **highlight** the words that are new to you.

② **Use** the sentence maker to ask your partner some questions. They should answer 'yes' or 'no'.

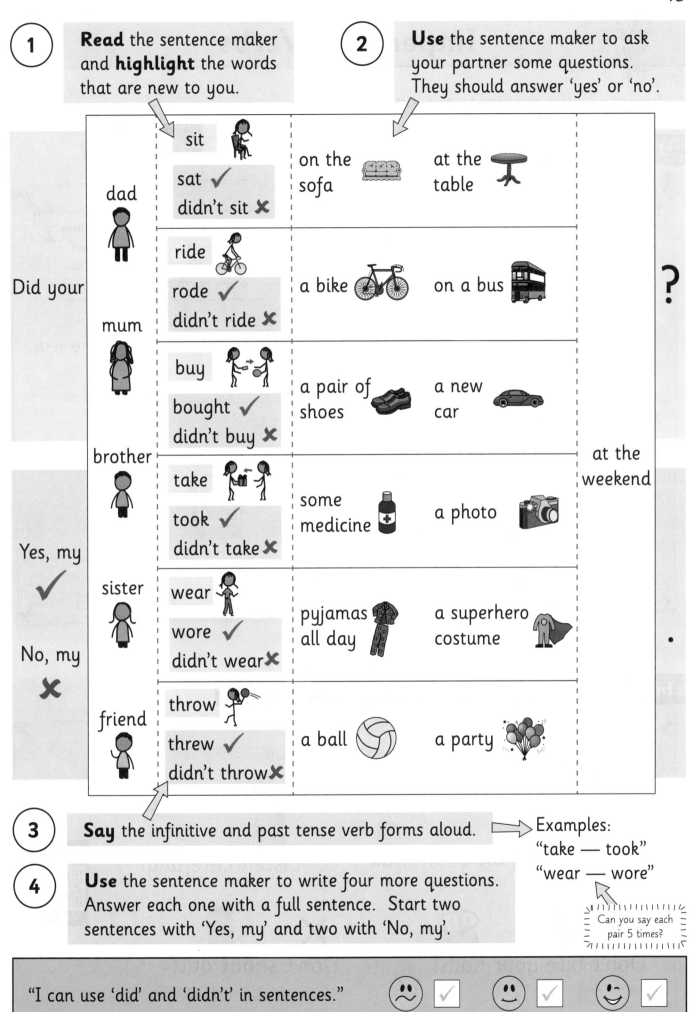

Did your

dad

sit / sat ✓ / didn't sit ✗ — on the sofa / at the table

mum

ride / rode ✓ / didn't ride ✗ — a bike / on a bus

buy / bought ✓ / didn't buy ✗ — a pair of shoes / a new car

brother

take / took ✓ / didn't take ✗ — some medicine / a photo

sister

wear / wore ✓ / didn't wear ✗ — pyjamas all day / a superhero costume

friend

throw / threw ✓ / didn't throw ✗ — a ball / a party

at the weekend

?

Yes, my ✓

No, my ✗

③ **Say** the infinitive and past tense verb forms aloud. → Examples: "take — took" "wear — wore"

Can you say each pair 5 times?

④ **Use** the sentence maker to write four more questions. Answer each one with a full sentence. Start two sentences with 'Yes, my' and two with 'No, my'.

"I can use 'did' and 'didn't' in sentences."

Section 7 — More Verbs

Imperative Verbs

Imperative verbs are used to give instructions.

Using IMPERATIVE VERBS

Imperative verbs are used to tell people **to do** or **not do** things.

Visit the dentist twice a year.

> In Spanish, 'I brush my teeth three times a day' is **me cepillo los dientes tres veces al día**. How do you say this in your language?

Imperative verbs don't have a subject — the sentence starts with the verb. The verb always takes the same form as the **infinitive**.

Add **don't** before the verb to tell people what **not to do**.

Don't forget to clean your teeth.

Listen & Repeat — Track 3

Don't eat sweets before bedtime.

Imperative sentences with EXCLAMATION MARKS

Imperative sentences are sometimes written with an **exclamation mark** to add emotion or urgency.

Stop rocking on your chair!

Listen carefully!

Listen & Repeat — Track 4

Don't bite your nails!

Don't shout out!

Hint for Helpers
Children could use these sentences to make a booklet on how to brush your teeth.

(1) **Number** the parts of the sentences in the correct order.

a) ☐ your | ☐ cold | [1] Wet | ☐ with | ☐ toothbrush | ☐ water.

b) ☐ on | ☐ Put | ☐ toothpaste | ☐ toothbrush. | ☐ your | ☐ some

c) ☐ and | ☐ your gum | ☐ from it. | ☐ sweep | ☐ Begin at | ☐ away

d) ☐ all | ☐ Clean | ☐ of | ☐ teeth. | ☐ the surfaces | ☐ of your

e) ☐ tongue. | ☐ forget | ☐ clean | ☐ your | ☐ to | ☐ Don't

f) ☐ for | ☐ brushing | ☐ two | ☐ minutes. | ☐ Continue

(2) **Choose** whether to end each sentence with a full stop or an exclamation mark. **Read** each sentence aloud to your partner — can they guess which punctuation you've used?

Hint for Helpers
See if children can identify the sentence that doesn't include the imperative.

Put the lid back on the toothpaste . / !

Stop squeezing the toothpaste from the top . / !

What beautiful, white teeth you have . / !

"I can make imperative sentences." ☹ ✓ ☺ ✓ 😉 ✓

Adverbials of Frequency & Place

You can use adverbials of frequency and place to say how often and where you do things.

Beach volleyball is a very popular sport in the USA. Rugby is very popular in the UK. Can you think of a popular sport in another country?

Adverbs of FREQUENCY show how often you do something

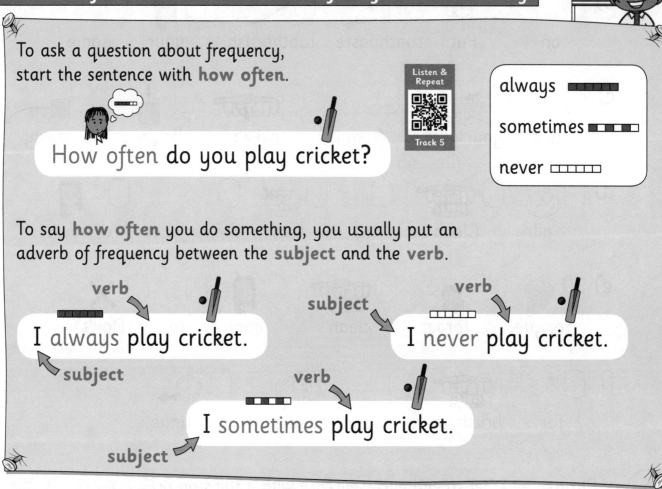

To ask a question about frequency, start the sentence with **how often**.

How often do you play cricket?

Listen & Repeat — Track 5

always
sometimes
never

To say **how often** you do something, you usually put an adverb of frequency between the **subject** and the **verb**.

verb

I always play cricket.

subject

subject

verb

I never play cricket.

verb

I sometimes play cricket.

subject

Adverbials of PLACE show where you do something

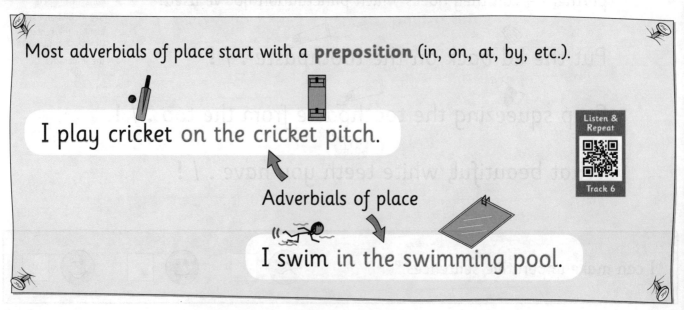

Most adverbials of place start with a **preposition** (in, on, at, by, etc.).

I play cricket on the cricket pitch.

Listen & Repeat — Track 6

Adverbials of place

I swim in the swimming pool.

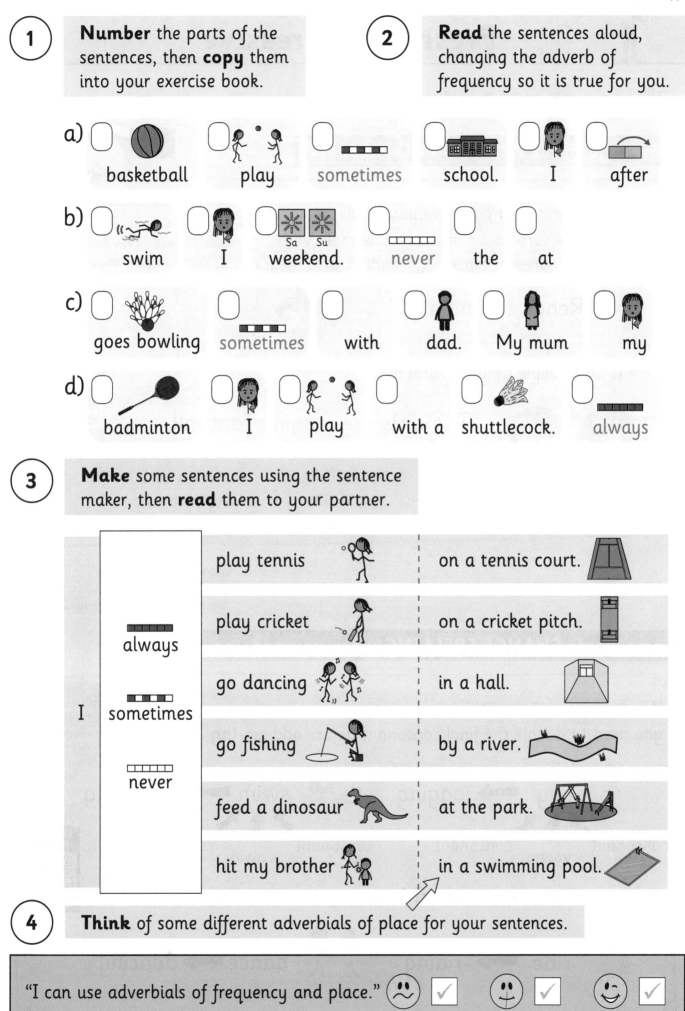

1 Number the parts of the sentences, then copy them into your exercise book.

2 Read the sentences aloud, changing the adverb of frequency so it is true for you.

a) ◯ basketball ◯ play ◯ sometimes ◯ school. ◯ I ◯ after

b) ◯ swim ◯ I ◯ weekend. (Sa Su) ◯ never ◯ the ◯ at

c) ◯ goes bowling ◯ sometimes ◯ with ◯ dad. ◯ My mum ◯ my

d) ◯ badminton ◯ I ◯ play ◯ with a shuttlecock. ◯ always

3 Make some sentences using the sentence maker, then read them to your partner.

I	always / sometimes / never	play tennis	on a tennis court.
		play cricket	on a cricket pitch.
		go dancing	in a hall.
		go fishing	by a river.
		feed a dinosaur	at the park.
		hit my brother	in a swimming pool.

4 Think of some different adverbials of place for your sentences.

"I can use adverbials of frequency and place." ☹ ✓ ☺ ✓ 😉 ✓

Section 7 — More Verbs

Present Progressive

The present progressive is used to talk about things happening right now.

How to form the PRESENT PROGRESSIVE

To form the present progressive you need:

the subject + the verb **to be** in the present tense + the main verb ending with **-ing**.

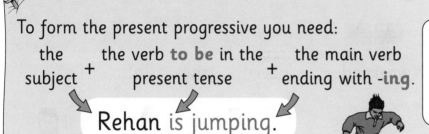

Rehan is jumping.

In Mandarin Chinese, 足球 (**zú qiú**) means 'football'. How do you say 'football' in your language?

....

Here is an example using a plural noun:

The girls are playing football.

the subject + the verb **to** be in the present tense + the main verb ending with **-ing**.

Listen & Repeat
Track 7

Hint for Helpers
The present tense forms of 'to be' are: 'I am', 'he / she / it is' and 'we / you / they are'.

Some words CHANGE SPELLING when you add -ing

When a verb ends in CVC (consonant — vowel — consonant), you need to double the final consonant before adding **-ing**.

Hint for Helpers
As shown on p.20, you don't double the consonant if the word ends in 'y', 'w' or 'x'

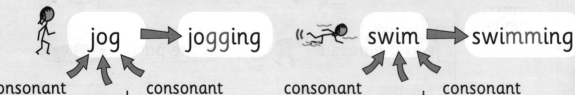

jog → jogging   swim → swimming

consonant vowel consonant   consonant vowel consonant

If the verb ends in **e**, remove the final **e** before adding **-ing**.

ride → riding   dance → dancing

Listen & Repeat
Track 8

1 **Read** the sentence maker, the play **charades** by acting out the activities.

I		swimming	dancing	running
He	am	bowling	cycling	fishing
She	is	sailing	skating	surfing

We			football	rugby	cricket
You	are	playing	volleyball	hockey	tennis
They			basketball	badminton	squash

2 **Draw** and **write** your favourite sentences.

Hint for Helpers
Children can draw and write more sentences in their exercise books.

3 **Write** the verbs in the correct part of the table with the suffix -ing.
Then use the verbs to **write** sentences in your exercise book.

serve   run   bounce   kick   dribble   bat

score   throw   hit   defend   catch

+ing	remove e +ing	double consonant +ing
throw**ing**	serv**ing**	run**ning**

"I can use the present progressive and add '-ing' to verbs."

Section 7 — More Verbs

'Going to' and 'Should'

You can use **going to** for talking about things you intend or want to do in the future. You use **should** to suggest good things for someone to do.

Going to

To form the future with **going to**, you need:

the verb **to be** in the present tense + **going to** + main verb in the infinitive

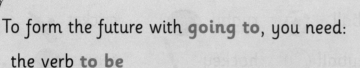

> In French, **je vais faire un gâteau** means 'I'm going to make a cake'. How do you say this in your language?
> ....

I am going to borrow a book from the library.

Listen & Repeat
Track 9

To make a negative sentence, you add **not** before **going to**.

At the weekend, we're not going to swim at the pool.

Hint for Helpers
Remind children that 'I'm', 'you're', 'he's', 'my friend's', etc. are contractions of a pronoun or noun and the verb 'to be'.

Should and Shouldn't

As with **going to**, you use **should** with a **verb** in the **infinitive**.

In the holidays, you should practise your times tables.

The negative form of **should** is **shouldn't** (should + not).

In the holidays, I shouldn't watch videos all day.

Listen & Repeat
Track 10

1 **Read** the sentence maker and **highlight** the words that are new to you.

In the holidays,	I'm / you're / my friend's / my brother's / we're / they're	going to / not going to	do	homework.	gardening.
			go to	the library.	the cinema.
			help	my mum.	my grandpa.
	I / you / my friend / my sister / my dad and I / my brothers	should / shouldn't	eat	take aways.	vegetables.
			tidy	the cupboard.	the garage.
			practise	times tables.	sport.
			buy	shoes.	school uniform.

2 **Draw** and **write** your favourite sentences.

Hint for Helpers
Encourage children to add their own ideas.

Going to

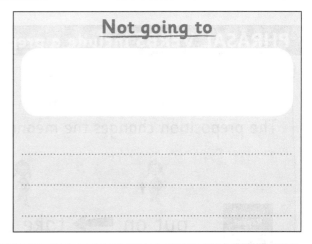
Not going to

3 Using the sentence maker, **draw** and **write** some sentences in your exercise book about what should and shouldn't happen during the holidays.

"I can talk about what's going to happen in the future."

Possessive Adjectives & Phrasal Verbs

Possessive adjectives and phrasal verbs can be useful for talking about the clothes you and other people wear.

POSSESSIVE ADJECTIVES go before nouns

You use different possessive adjectives depending on who the thing belongs to.

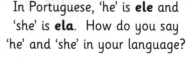

In Portuguese, 'he' is **ele** and 'she' is **ela**. How do you say 'he' and 'she' in your language?

....

 I ➜ my   he ➜ his

 she ➜ her   you ➜ your

 they ➜ their   we ➜ our

Hint for Helpers
Children can associate the possessive adjective with the personal pronouns to help remember them.

Listen & Repeat
Track 1

They always wear their school uniform.

You sometimes wear your sports kit.

Hint for Helpers
It's common for children to confuse 'his' with 'he's' ('he is'). Check that they know the difference.

PHRASAL VERBS include a preposition

Some verbs are sometimes written with a preposition. The preposition changes the meaning of the verb.

Hint for Helpers
Phrasal verbs can be confusing for children with EAL who may only recognise the root verb.

Listen & Repeat
Track 2

put on ➜ take off   do up ➜ undo

pull up ➜ pull down   button up ➜ unbutton

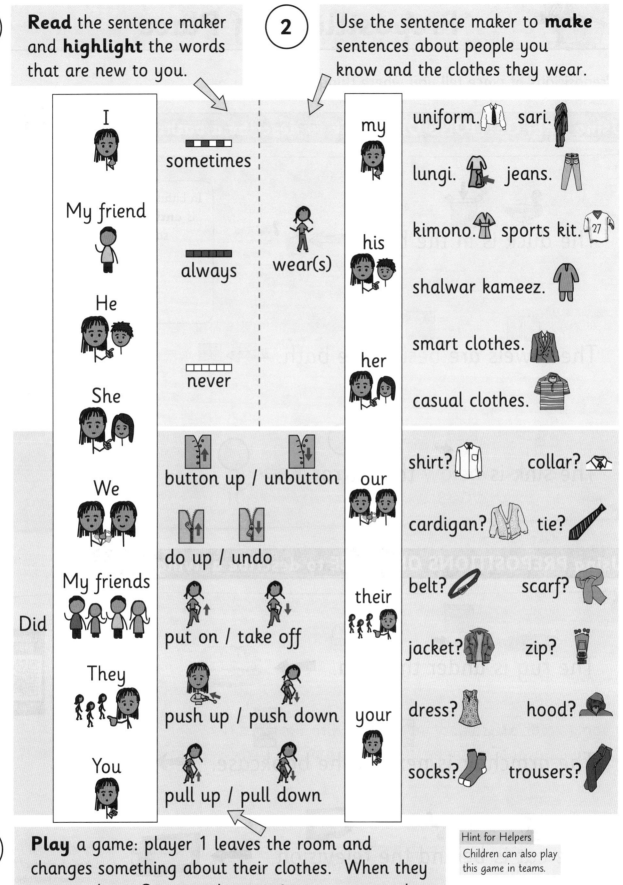

1 **Read** the sentence maker and **highlight** the words that are new to you.

2 Use the sentence maker to **make** sentences about people you know and the clothes they wear.

3 **Play** a game: player 1 leaves the room and changes something about their clothes. When they return, player 2 must ask **questions** to guess what they did. Use the sentence maker to help you.

Hint for Helpers
Children can also play this game in teams.

"I can talk about the clothes I wear and the clothes other people wear."

Prepositions of Place

Prepositions of place tell you where things are.

Using PREPOSITIONS OF PLACE to describe a bathroom

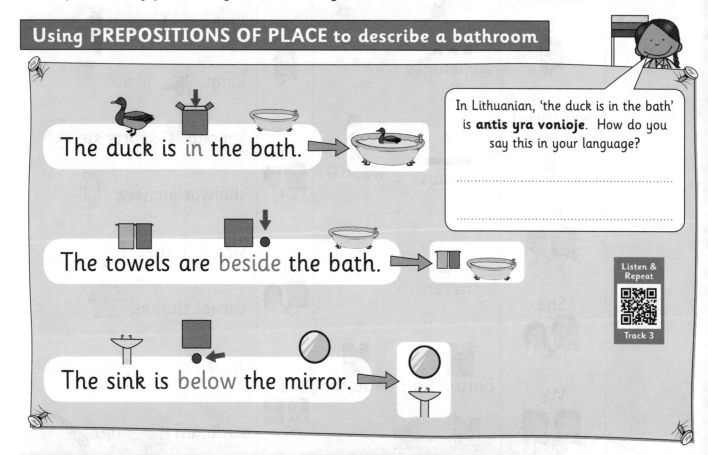

The duck is in the bath.

In Lithuanian, 'the duck is in the bath' is **antis yra vonioje**. How do you say this in your language?

The towels are beside the bath.

The sink is below the mirror.

Listen & Repeat
Track 3

Using PREPOSITIONS OF PLACE to describe a living room

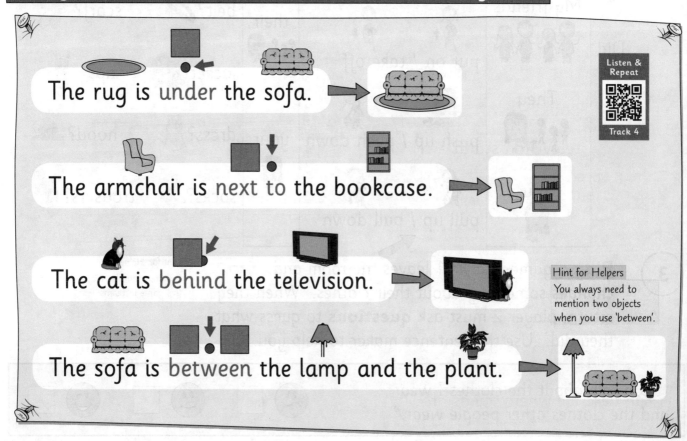

Listen & Repeat
Track 4

The rug is under the sofa.

The armchair is next to the bookcase.

The cat is behind the television.

Hint for Helpers
You always need to mention two objects when you use 'between'.

The sofa is between the lamp and the plant.

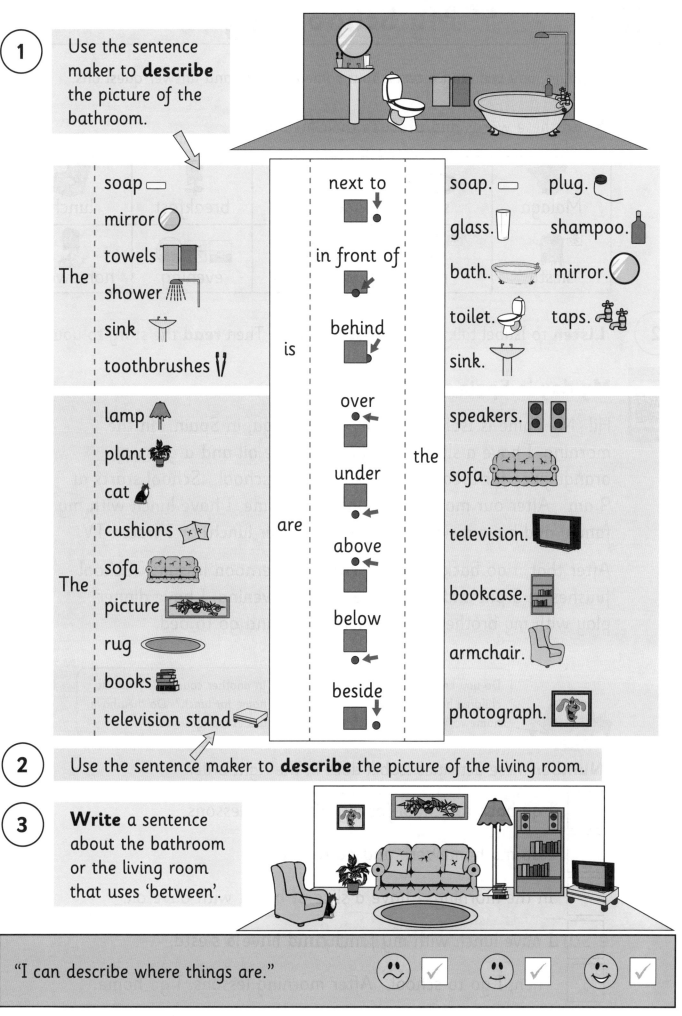

1 Use the sentence maker to **describe** the picture of the bathroom.

The
soap ⬭
mirror ◯
towels 🖼
shower 🚿
sink 🚰
toothbrushes 𝄃𝄃

is

next to ⬛↓●
in front of ⬛●
behind ⬛

over ●⬛
under ⬛●
above ●⬛
below ⬛●
beside ⬛↓●

are

the

soap. ⬭   plug. 🔌
glass. 🥛   shampoo. 🍾
bath. 🛁   mirror. ◯
toilet. 🚽   taps. 🚰
sink. 🚰

speakers. 🔊🔊
sofa. 🛋
television. 📺
bookcase. 📚
armchair. 🪑
photograph. 🖼

2 Use the sentence maker to **describe** the picture of the living room.

3 **Write** a sentence about the bathroom or the living room that uses 'between'.

"I can describe where things are." 🙁 ✓ 🙂 ✓ 😉 ✓

Section 8 — Possessives, Adverbs and Prepositions

My School Day

On these pages, you will read a text about someone's day and answer questions.

1 **Read** these words and **discuss** their meanings.

Malaga	slice	olive oil	breakfast	lunch
siesta	nap	afternoon	evening	homework

2 **Listen** to Isabel talk about her school day. Then **read** the story to yourself.

Audio
Track 1

My day in Spain

Hi! My name is Isabel and I live in Malaga, in Spain. In the morning, I have a slice of bread with olive oil and a glass of orange juice for breakfast. Then, I go to school. School starts at 9 am. After our morning lessons, I go home, I have lunch with my family and have a siesta (a short nap after lunch) or I watch TV.

After that, I go back to school for my afternoon lessons. School finishes at 5 pm and I go home. In the evening, I have dinner, play with my brother, do my homework and go to bed.

Do you know about a typical school day in another country? What do children have for breakfast? Do they go home for lunch? Do they have homework every day? Do they have lessons in the afternoon?

3 **Number** these activities Isabel does in the right order.

☐ I go back to school for my afternoon lessons.

☐ I do my homework and go to bed.

☐ In the morning, I have a slice of bread with olive oil.

☐ I have lunch with my family and have a siesta.

☐ Then, I go to school. After morning lessons, I go home.

4 **Correct** the sentences below.

a) Her name is Malaga. ➡ No, her name is ....

b) She lives in Pakistan. ➡ No, she lives in ....

c) She has lunch with her friends at school.

....

....

d) She goes back to school for sports practice.

....

....

5 **Circle** the correct answers.

What does Isabel drink at breakfast time?
a) a slice of bread   b) bread with olive oil   c) a glass of orange juice

What time does school start?
a) 9 am   b) 10 am   c) 8 am

What does Isabel do next after morning lessons?
a) goes to school   b) goes home   c) has afternoon lessons

What is a siesta?
a) a snack   b) a television programme   c) a short nap

When does Isabel play with her brother?
a) in the morning   b) in the afternoon   c) in the evening

6 **Answer** these questions in your exercise book.

Why do you think people in Spain have a siesta?

Do you think you would like to go to school in Spain? Why or why not?

"I can answer questions about someone's day at school."

Numbers 30-100

These pages teach how to pronounce the numbers 30-100 and the vocabulary needed to do basic calculations.

COUNTING to 100 and using GREATER and LESS than symbols

These are the multiples of 10 from 30 to 100.

30 thirty	70 seventy
40 forty	80 eighty
50 fifty	90 ninety
60 sixty	100 one hundred

In French, 80 is **quatre-vingts**, which means 'four twenties'. How do you say 80 in your language?

....

Make sure you say the '**-ty**' sound like the letter **t** so it sounds different to the '**-teen**' sound in numbers like thir**teen** (13).

You can join these multiples of 10 with a number from 1 to 9 to say any number up to 99.

64 sixty-four

The symbol > means **greater than** and the symbol < means **less** than.

91 is greater than 19 ➡ 91 > 19 ⬅ The crocodile mouth always opens to the **bigger number**.

13 is less than 31 ➡ 13 < 31

31 is equal to 31 ➡ 31 = 31

Listen & Repeat

Track 1

ADDING, SUBTRACTING and finding the DIFFERENCE

Increasing and **decreasing** numbers means **adding** and **subtracting**.

Increase 20 by 8 ➡ 20 + 8 = 28

Decrease 40 by 10 ➡ 40 − 10 = 30

Listen & Repeat

Track 2

Subtract the smaller number from the bigger number to find the **difference** between them.

Find the difference between 25 and 15 ➡ 25 − 15 = 10

(1) **Listen** to some number sentences. **Write** them in your exercise book using digits and symbols. **Tick** them if they are true.

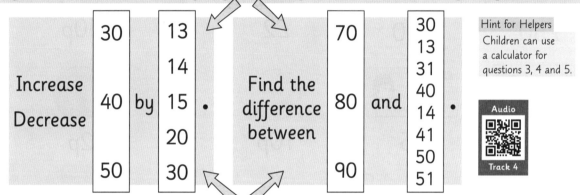

17		17		60		60
70	<	70		61	<	61
71		71		16		16
13		13		41		41
30	>	30		14	>	14
31	=	31		40	=	40

Hint for Helpers
Make sure children can tell the difference between, for example, 17 (seven**teen**) and 70 (seven**ty**).

Audio
Track 3

(2) **Write** some of your own number sentences and **read** them to your partner so they can **write** them. Discuss whether the sentences are **true** or **false**.

(3) **Listen** to the number sentences and their answers. **Write** them in your exercise book using digits and symbols. **Tick** them if they are true.

| Increase Decrease | | 30 40 50 | by | 13 14 15 20 30 | . | Find the difference between | 70 80 90 | and | 30 13 31 40 14 41 50 51 | . |

Hint for Helpers
Children can use a calculator for questions 3, 4 and 5.

Audio
Track 4

(4) **Write** some more number sentences and their answers. **Read** them to your partner so they can **write** them. Discuss whether they are **true** or **false**.

(5) **Answer** the questions below in your exercise book.

a) There are 17 ladybirds on a leaf. The number increases by 7. How many ladybirds are there now?

b) Maria has 30 marbles. She drops them and loses some. Her marbles decrease in number by 14. How many marbles does she have left?

c) Jan is 90 cm tall and Alif is 81 cm tall. What is the difference between their heights?

"I can count to 100, use the symbols '>' and '<' and find the difference between numbers."

Money

These pages teach the words for talking about British money and how to ask for the price of things.

British money is called POUNDS

Money uses the symbols **£** and **p**.

£10 → **ten** pounds   50p → **fifty** pence

In Brazil, the money we use is called **Real**. In Poland it's called **złoty**. Do you know what money in another country is called?

Notes:

£50

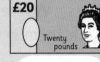
£20

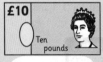
£10

£5

Coins:

£2

£1

50p

20p

10p

5p

2p

1p

Hint for Helpers
The singular form of 'pence' is 'penny'.

You don't say 'pence' if the price is greater than £1.

£1.30 → **one pound thirty**

Hint for Helpers
Make sure children understand the word order and don't say 'pound one thirty'.

Listen & Repeat
Track 5

How to ask for the PRICE of something

Use **is** to ask how much one thing costs.

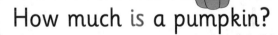

How much is a pumpkin?   **A pumpkin is £3.**

Listen & Repeat
Track 6

Use **are** to ask how much more than one thing costs.

How much are the grapes?   **The grapes are £1.50.**

Section 10 — Maths Language

1 Use the sentence maker to **tell** your partner the price of the pineapple and the oranges.

£1.05

70p

One	pound	five
Two		eight
Three		twelve
Seventeen	pounds	thirty-two
Twenty-seven		fifty
Thirty-two		seventy-five
Seventy		ninety-nine
	pence	

2 **Choose** a price for these fruits and vegetables.
Write the price in words. Use the sentence maker to help you.

lettuce: ....

bananas: ....
....

potatoes: ....

mango: ....
....

How much	is a		?
	are the		

	pineapple	oranges
	melon	onions
	lettuce	bananas
	mango	potatoes

A		is	£.................. .
The		are	

3 With a partner, **ask** and **say** how much the fruits and vegetables are.
Write one of the questions and answers below.

....
....
....

"I can ask for and give the price of things."   😟 ✓   🙂 ✓   😉 ✓

Vowel Sounds

Children with EAL can struggle to hear and pronounce English long vowel sounds.
These pages introduce them to a common written form of all the vowel sounds in English.

short vowel sound   long vowel sound

Listen & Repeat — Track 1

a   apple

ai   rain

Listen & Repeat — Track 2

> **Hint for Helpers**
> Show children that they need to say the letter name (a = 'ay') of the first vowel in the grapheme to find the sound of the long vowel.

e   elephant

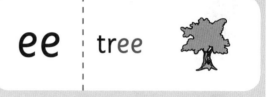

ee   tree

i   igloo

igh   night

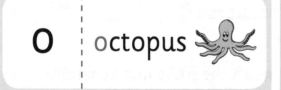

o   octopus

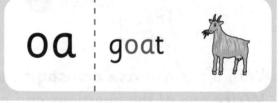

oa   goat

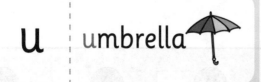

u   umbrella

ue   argue

These are example graphemes for the remaining vowel sounds, plus a few important letter combinations that can be difficult for children with EAL.

  Track 3

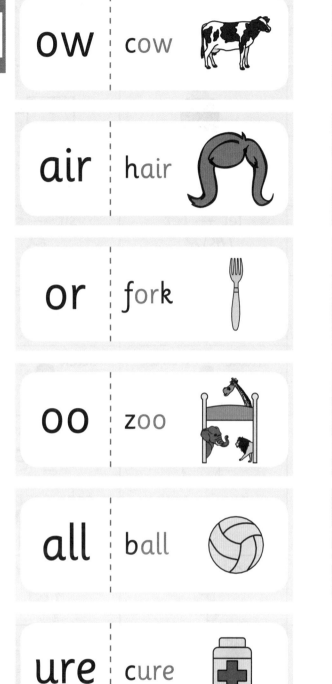

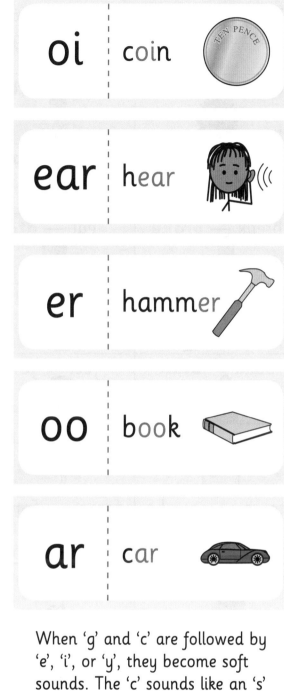

ow cow | **oi** coin

air hair | **ear** hear

or fork | **er** hammer

oo zoo | **oo** book

all ball | **ar** car

ure cure

When 'g' and 'c' are followed by 'e', 'i', or 'y', they become soft sounds. The 'c' sounds like an 's' and the 'g' sounds like a 'j'.

  Track 4

 city | centre | cycle |  giant | gem | gym

"I can tell the difference between long and short vowels."

Phonics and Verb Table

Table of Irregular Verbs

This page is a reference tool to help children with EAL learn irregular verbs in the simple past tense. Children can use this page to help them as they work through the book.

be — **was / were**	draw — **drew**	hide — **hid**	send — **sent**
blow — **blew**	drink — **drank**	hold — **held**	sing — **sang**
break — **broke**	eat — **ate**	let — **let**	sit — **sat**
bring — **brought**	fall — **fell**	lose — **lost**	sleep — **slept**
build — **built**	feel — **felt**	make — **made**	stick — **stuck**
buy — **bought**	find — **found**	meet — **met**	swim — **swam**
catch — **caught**	forget — **forgot**	put — **put**	take — **took**
choose — **chose**	get — **got**	read — **read**	teach — **taught**
come — **came**	give — **gave**	ride — **rode**	tell — **told**
cut — **cut**	go — **went**	run — **ran**	think — **thought**
do — **did**	have — **had**	say — **said**	wear — **wore**
dream — **dreamt**	hear — **heard**	see — **saw**	write — **wrote**

Phonics and Verb Table